SPARK ISLAND

CW00420169

KS2 National Tests
ENGLISH
Learning Adventures

Contents

* Texts for the practice reading test can be found between pages 21 and 28.
For ease of use, this section can be taken out of the book.

Anne Loadman

Introduction

The National Tests

The National Tests take place in May of each year. The tests for Key Stage 2 are in English, Mathematics and Science and are administered over the course of a week. The tests are marked by external examiners and the scripts are returned to the school at the beginning of July. The marks for each paper are totalled and a Level is given, usually between 3 and 5. Level 4 is the average level to be achieved by an 11-year-old.

The English Test is divided into two main parts: the Reading Test and the Writing Test.

The Reading Test lasts for 60 minutes: 15 minutes for reading a booklet of different text types, followed by a period of 45 minutes, in which a series of comprehension questions must be answered. This activity accounts for 50 per cent of the total English Test marks, therefore it is vital that children have practice in this area before the test. The questions range from simple recall and location of information from the text, to more complex types, where the child's opinion is asked for. The test demands a competent reading ability and regular daily reading practice is beneficial, especially followed by conversation about the text.

The Writing Test is made up of two writing tasks (which include a mark for handwriting) and a spelling test. From 2003, handwriting will no longer be assessed separately, so it is important that children have a clear, legible, joined style well in advance of the tests. From 2003, spelling carries a possible seven marks and is administered by the teacher who reads a passage to the children and they supply the correct spellings to fill in blanks in the passage.

The majority of marks will be awarded for the two writing tasks: one longer, one shorter. From 2003, there will be no choice of activity in the test. However in this book a choice of activity has been given so that a wider range of writing types may be covered.

This book aims to give practice and advice on all aspects of the test, but focuses mainly on the reading comprehension and the writing tasks (pages 4-32), followed by an authentic-feeling practice test (pages 37-45) for which paper may be required. Guidance for assessing your child's level of achievement is also included (page 46).

(see page 45)

This text is to be read twice to your child. The child should attempt the spellings at the second reading.

THE SOLAR SYSTEM

The solar system in <u>which</u> we live is made up of the Sun, its planets, natural satellites, asteroids, meteoroids and comets. Each of these <u>bodies</u> are held to each other by the force we <u>call</u> gravity. The Sun is by far the most <u>important</u> part of the solar system. It is our nearest star. Without the Sun there would be no <u>light</u> and no <u>life</u> on Earth.

The other main members of the solar system are the nine major planets. The planets are Mercury, Venus, Earth, Mars, Jupiter, Saturn, Uranus, Neptune and Pluto.

The planets are <u>moving</u> in almost <u>circular</u> orbits based on the force of gravity. The Sun's gravitational pull is the most <u>powerful</u> gravitational force in the solar system.

The planets orbit the Sun in the same anticlockwise direction. A planet's year is the time <u>required</u> for it to complete one full orbit <u>around</u> the Sun. This varies in length from planet to planet. One Earth year lasts $365\frac{1}{4}$ days.

The planets are <u>grouped</u> according to their physical properties. The inner planets (Mercury, Venus, Earth and Mars) are called the terrestrial (meaning earthlike) planets. They are dense and small in <u>size</u>. They have solid, rocky crusts and <u>their</u> insides are made of molten, metallic rocks. Most of the nine major planets have one or more moons. In 1969, Neil Armstrong was the first man to <u>walk</u> on the moon which orbits our Earth.

The planets Jupiter, Saturn, Uranus and Neptune are sometimes <u>known</u> as the 'gas <u>giants</u>'. Jupiter, is famous for its 'red spot': the site of a huge storm on the planet. Saturn, of course, is famous for its rings. It has been said that if you had a bath large <u>enough</u>, Saturn could float in it because of its low density. Pluto is on the <u>edge</u> of our Solar System and is hard to see clearly, even with modern <u>telescopes</u>.

Allow one mark for each correct answer.

3

Reading practice

In the Reading Test you will be asked to find words, copy phrases, match things and write your own opinion. In this section you can practise all the different kinds of questions you are likely to meet.

Multiple-choice questions

For these questions, you are given a choice of four or five answers and you must circle the correct answer. The information to answer these questions can usually be found in the story or passage and are usually facts.

Here is an example:

> Chloe had forgotten her homework – again! She was very worried because she knew she would be in trouble when it was time to hand it in. Mr Rogers made you stay in at playtime if you forgot it twice in a row. She knew exactly where she had left it – on the table beside the door, but there was no time to go back for it now. Why did she have to be so absent-minded? It was no good; she would just have to think of a good excuse. She had already used the one about her dog chewing it up; and the one about the homework having gone in the washing machine. What could she say? Then, all of a sudden, it came to her – she would pretend to feel sick and then the teacher would forget all about her homework. Brilliant! Or so she thought.

The passage is about:

someone who doesn't feel well   (a girl who has forgotten her homework)   a dog that has eaten some homework   doing the washing.

Now you try.

Chloe decided she would

| 1 | tell the teacher the truth | not go to school | pretend that she was sick | make up an excuse. |

Mr Rogers

| 2 | didn't mind if you forgot your homework | gave lots of homework | shouted at you if you forgot your homework | kept you in if you forgot your homework twice. |

Finding words

Don't rely on your memory. Always look at the text.

Sometimes you are asked to find and copy a word or a phrase from the text. To answer this type of question you need to reread the passage carefully and find the right word.

Here is an example:

Question: Find and copy a word that shows that Chloe thought she had had a good idea.
Answer: Brilliant!

This would give you one mark.

Now you try.
1   Find and copy a word from the text which is similar in meaning to forgetful.

2   Find a word in the text that shows how Chloe is feeling about forgetting her homework.

3   Can you find a word or phrase in the text to show that Chloe had forgotten her homework before?

Snakes

Snakes are reptiles, whose closest relatives are lizards. Many scientists believe that snakes developed from lizards millions of years ago. Lots of people are frightened of snakes but in Britain there is only one naturally occurring poisonous snake, the viper, sometimes called the adder.

The Ancient Greeks regarded the snake as a symbol of healing because of its ability to shed its old skin and grow a new one.

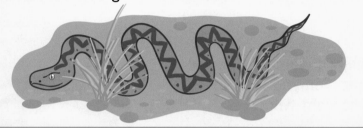

Some passages will be **non-fiction** texts like this one.

1   Choose the best group of words to fit the passage and put a circle around your choice.

The Ancient Greeks

| were scared of snakes | kept snakes as pets | thought the snake represented healing | used snakes as medicine. |

2   Find and copy a word that means the family of animals to which snakes and lizards belong.

   ....

3   What is the only poisonous type of snake to live in Britain?

   ....

4   What does the word 'shed' mean in this passage?

   ....

Sequencing or matching

If there are illustrations, use the clues that they provide as well.

You may be asked to sequence some events or actions, or to fill in tables to match dates or people.

1 Read this passage and answer the sequencing question that follows.

In Sparkopolis, all was quiet. It was evening and most of the inhabitants were at home, preparing their evening meal. However, a band of Malvos were out to cause mischief. They started by blowing up and bursting balloons, then moved on to teasing the Spironauts by hiding their jet packs. Still not content, they moved towards one of the Crombies' houses, where the Crombies were inside reading quietly. The Malvos made loud noises in the street and disturbed them. Everyone came out to see what was going on.

By the time the Elders heard about the disturbance, the Malvos had disappeared so the Gang offered to track them down. They knew all the Malvos' hiding places and soon caught up with them. The Elders made the mischievous Malvos clean up all their mess and the ringleaders were put in prison for a week.

2 Number these events in the order in which they appear in the passage.

The Malvos went to the Crombies' house. ☐

The Malvos had to do jobs for a week. ☐

The Gang went to look for the Malvos. ☐

The Malvos burst balloons. ☐

Everyone came out to see what was going on. ☐

The Malvos hid the Spironauts' jetpacks. ☐

It was quiet in Sparkopolis. ☐

3 Now match up these events and actions with the characters who carried them out. Draw a line to connect the correct characters and actions.

The Malvos   reading quietly

The Malvos   found the Malvos

The Crombies   heard about the disturbance

The Gang   bursting balloons

The Elders   hiding jetpacks

4   Now read this non-fiction text.

THANKS TO SCIENCE

- Isaac Newton lived from 1642 to 1727. He is known as the 'Father of Modern Science'. Between 1664 and 1666 he was responsible for finding out that light is made up of different colours, and explained the theory of gravity.

- Michael Faraday (1791-1867) became famous for his work on electricity. In 1831 he built the world's first dynamo, to produce an electric current. Imagine what the world would be like today without electrical devices.

- Louis Pasteur (1822-1895) was a scientist who found out that diseases are caused by the bacteria we call germs. Before this, scientists thought that diseases were caused by bad smells! Around 1881, he also found out how to use tiny amounts of germs to vaccinate people against diseases. This saved a lot of lives.

- Galileo Galilei (1564-1642) was a clever mathematician who was also interested in astronomy. In 1610 he wrote a book saying that the planets orbited the Sun. Before this, people believed that the Earth stayed still and the planets travelled round us. Even after his discovery, people still didn't believe him!

5   Use the information above to fill in this table.

Name of scientist	Main discovery/invention	Date of discovery
Michael Faraday		1831
	Planets orbited the Sun	1610
	Light is made of different colours	
Louis Pasteur	Principles of vaccination	

6   Which of the above was the earliest discovery?

7 (a) How old was each of the above scientists when he made his discovery?

(b)   Who lived the longest?

8   Which do you think was the most important discovery and why?

You will be asked questions about the layout of the text.

1   Read the text and answer the questions below.

HiYa! Magazine

A weekly look into the lives of the rich and famous of Sparkopolis.

THIS WEEK'S FEATURES:

* Unicycles – fad or forever?
* Nina reveals winter fashion secrets!
* EXCLUSIVE interview with Strat and the Gang – Sparkopolis' newest residents speak out!

ALSO IN THIS WEEK'S ISSUE:

* Looking after your books – a Crombie's guide.
* How to tame a Xybok.
* Sparkanon – plans for an extension – we have a peek at the plans!

PLUS

All the regular features: Horoscopes, Problem Page and all Sparkopolis Radio and TV listings!

WHEN YOU SAY 'HiYa!' TO HiYa!
YOU SAY 'GOODBYE' TO BOREDOM!

Reminder

* Make sure you know all the correct terms such as: headlines or italics.
* Think about why the text has been organized in a particular way.
* Look at the whole page of text and see how the items have been laid out.
* Look at words in bold or CAPITALS.
* Are there any arrows or numbers to lead you from one section to another?
* Are there tables or charts, or is the work organized into paragraphs with subtitles?

2   The words HiYa! Magazine are in large bold print. Why is this?

3 (a) How is the information about this week's articles organized?

(b)   Why do you think it has been organized in this way?

4   Why are words such as EXCLUSIVE and PLUS in capital letters?

Longer questions or opinions

Put as much detail as you can into these answers to get maximum marks.

Sometimes you will be asked to write a short paragraph for an answer giving your opinion about something, comparing two articles or talking about the language the author has used.

Here is an example:

Look at the information about HiYa! Magazine on page 9 and write about the way the author has tried to grab the reader's attention.

Here is one answer:
'I think the author has used coloured headings to grab your attention and tell us what is going to be on the inside.'

This answer is not wrong, but it is not detailed enough.
Look at another answer to the same task.
'The author has used coloured headings in capitals for the headlines to grab the reader's attention and then listed this week's contents in bullet points so that it is clear what is going to be inside. The author also uses words like exclusive to make you think that no other magazine has got these articles.'

The second answer is more detailed and would get more marks than the first one.

Remember
If there are three marks available for a question, try to think of at least three comments to make or pieces of information to include.

1 Look at this question.
   Would you enjoy reading HiYa! Magazine? Give reasons for your choice.
This question asks for your opinion, so look at the text again and make notes. These questions might help you to plan your answer:
• Would I enjoy it or not?
• What would I enjoy/not enjoy about it?
• Can I compare it to other similar texts I have read?
• What would make it more interesting to me?
• Which part of the text did I find most interesting?

2 Now try and answer the question above for yourself.

_____

_____

_____

3 When you read a book or any text, ask yourself an 'opinion' question about it and try to answer it in your head or write it down.

Writing practice

Strat's tips

There are two writing tasks to complete in the Tests. One will be fiction (story or narrative writing) and one non-fiction writing. In this section you will find some ideas and tips for improving your narrative writing.

Planning your story

It can be helpful to use a planning sheet. In the tests there will be space for you to plan your writing and some suggestions about what you need to think about. You can make your own planning sheet on the test paper if you want. Here is a very simple planning sheet you can use:

- Read the title carefully and make sure your story fits the title.
- Don't have too many characters (3 or 4 main characters at most).
- Plan how your story will begin and end and what will happen (the plot).
- Think about where your story will take place.
- Jot down useful describing words and phrases.

Story title	
Characters In this space write down who will be in your story and write a brief description of each character. Write notes about their personality as well as their appearance.	**Settings** In this space write notes about where your story will take place and jot down some good words which will help you to describe the different settings.
Plot In this space write about what will happen in your story (the events) and in which order they will come. You can also use this space to organize your writing into paragraphs and say briefly what will happen in each.	**Beginning and ending** It is very important that your story has an interesting start to capture the reader's imagination and an equally good ending to tie up all the threads of your story. Use this space to plan your opening sentence and your final sentence(s).

Characters

Your story needs to have strong characters who come to life through your writing. You need to make the reader feel that they can see the characters you write about.

Here are some ideas about what you need to include to make your stories great.

You can do this by:
- describing what the characters look like
- describing the character's personality
- using the way the character speaks and acts to tell us more about them.

Look at this character description of Nina.

Appearance: likes to wear jeans and trainers; hair usually tied back; slim build, large eyes.
Personality: outgoing, bright and cheerful; sensible most of the time but also adventurous and tough.

Once you have a character description it helps you to think about how that character will act and speak in your story. It also helps to add interest if you have characters with different personalities.

Remember

Describe their personalities as well as their appearance.

Make notes first.

Write a paragraph describing each character.

Read them to someone to see if they can guess who you have written about!

Now it's your turn.

1   Write a character description of two people you know well. It could be two of your friends or two members of your family. One could even be a pet!

One of the characters in your story could be you!

Lost!

Danger!

The Time Traveller

2   Here are some story titles. Think of two or three characters you might write about in each story and make notes about their appearance and personalities.

The Great Sparkopolis Library Mystery

Keep out!

Setting

The setting is where your story takes place. There may be more than one setting, e.g. your bedroom, the street, your school, the town. It is a good idea to describe your surroundings so that the reader can feel as if they are there too.

1   Read the description of Sparkopolis and see if you can imagine it for yourself.

> Sparkopolis is the capital city of Spark Island. It was built by the Elders who love experimenting with architecture, so the whole city is full of weird and imaginative buildings. There are many magnificent libraries, filled with rows of books of every kind imaginable. Some books, almost as old as time itself, line the solid wooden shelves of the Ancient Texts section, whilst brand new books are delivered nearly every day and wait in boxes, ready to be displayed. In Sparkopolis, everyone enjoys reading.
>
> But by far the biggest building in Sparkopolis is the Sparkanon, home of the Elders. It can be seen from all over the city and shines in both sunlight and moonlight. Its mysterious towers and spires hold secrets that many on Spark Island would like to discover.

2   Write a description of a setting. Choose somewhere you know well to start with, e.g. your bedroom.

Remember
Settings can be about sounds you hear, as well as what you can see.

_____

_____

_____

_____

You can put in a paragraph describing the setting when you move from place to place. These paragraphs don't have to be long, but they help to give the reader a mental picture of the scene.

3   Choose some of the settings below and write some interesting words and phrases you could use to describe them. Then write a description as a whole paragraph.
   • You wake up one morning and it has snowed overnight. Describe what you see.
   • You are on a lonely beach at sunset. Describe your surroundings.
   • You are in a busy town centre with lots of traffic and shoppers. Describe the sights and sounds around you.
   • You are all alone in an old house. Describe the sights and sounds you experience.

Plot

The plot of a story is all the events and action that make your story interesting.

1   Imagine you are going to write a story called 'The Rescue'.
Plan out your plot using the guidelines below.
Remember to write in note form.

Beginning: ....
....
....

Event 1: ....
....
....

Event 2: ....
....
....

Event 3: ....
....
....

Ending ....
....
....

2   Now your plot is planned, try writing out the whole story in your notebook or on some paper.

3   Here are some more suggestions for story titles.
Try planning the plot for them in the same way as above.

- Don't try and plan too many events. You won't have time and the plot can become confusing. Stick to 2 or 3 main events and write about them well.

- Use the plot to plan your writing in paragraphs. When a scene or the action changes, start a new paragraph. Think like a film director!

- Conversations can be used to move the plot along, but keep them interesting.

Remember to plan your characters and the setting too.

The Mystery of Doom Castle

Shipwrecked!   Lost and Alone

14

Beginnings

Grab the reader's attention with a really good story start. Think about what kind of story you are writing and plan your opening sentence.

Don't always start in the same way. You can start with a flashback, with dialogue, in the middle of some action or by setting the scene.

Here are some examples.

Flashback
It didn't seem very long since the Malvos had tried to sabotage the last raspberry harvest. Nina remembered she had only found out about their plans by accident the day before picking started.

Dialogue
'Come on, we'll be late!' Nina shouted.
'Late for what?' inquired a sleepy Dotty.
'Late for the competition!' Nina reminded her.

Action/Setting the scene
Flash! Bang! Brilliant light shot through the closed curtains, lighting up the room, followed by a huge booming sound that reminded Dotty of a giant's voice. It was the worst thunderstorm Spark Island had seen for years and Milo and Strat were somewhere outside!

All of these beginnings want to make you read on and find out what happens next.

1   Plan the opening sentences for these story titles using a different kind of start for each one:
   • The Storm
   • Attacked by Bees!
   • Forest Adventure

Endings

Endings have to be planned with equal care. Tie up all the loose ends in your story and make the reader think you have taken as much care over the end as the beginning.

Or, you could leave the audience guessing by writing a cliff-hanger, an uncertain ending, but this needs to be planned carefully or else it looks as though you have just stopped writing.

Here are some examples of endings:

It was hard to believe that only a few hours ago, everything had been so different. Dotty sat back on the settee and thought about the day's events. The adventure the Gang had experienced hardly seemed real now, but the photograph in her hand was proof. What an amazing day!

A cliff-hanger

So it seemed as though the whole matter was settled. The Xybok had gone back to grazing on the plains, the Crombies had rearranged their study and peace reigned once more on Spark Island. Only one small doubt remained in Zeb's mind, it was something he had read about the Malvos. But there weren't enough of them … or were there?

1   Plan your own endings to the three story titles given on page 15. Then write one as a cliff-hanger.

Interviews and play scripts

You might be asked to write in the style of an interview or a play script. Both are similar in the way they are set out.

Interviews

An interview is when someone asks another person questions and their responses are written down.

Here is an interview that Nina carried out with Zeb.

Nina:	Zeb, you know so many interesting facts. How did you become so clever?
Zeb:	Well, I have always been interested in learning since I was very small.
Nina:	Is there any subject that interests you more than others?
Zeb:	I have always been interested in animals, especially insects. I used to have an ant farm when I was younger.
Nina:	An ant farm! Wasn't that rather unusual?
Zeb:	I suppose so, but we weren't allowed pets at Grunge Hall and the ants just lived in the garden. I was fascinated by them.

Notice how the names of the speakers are put on the left-hand side of the page and are followed by a colon (:). The questions follow on from each other, as if the interviewer is really listening to the person being interviewed.

Now you try.
1   Interview one of your family or friends about:
   • their favourite team or music
   • what it was like when they were at school
   • their pets.
   Make notes or record the interview on a cassette.

2   Write it up. Set it out like a proper interview.

Play scripts

Play scripts are similar to interviews in the way they are set out, with the character's name on the left-hand side of the page, next to the words they say. But there are extra things to add. In plays the actors need to know how they have to say a line and how they should be acting, as well as when to come on and leave the stage. These extra bits of information are the 'stage directions'.

Scene 1 – In the living room. The table is set for a meal. The TV is on.
Chloe: Are you coming swimming today?
Stefi: *(Ignoring her)* Steven, can I borrow that new CD from you?
Steven: *(Trying to watch the TV)* All right, but don't lose it!
Chloe: *(Getting angry)* Stefi, I asked you if you were coming to the swimming pool!
Stefi: *(Sorting through the CDs)* I know you did! *(she pauses)* I might.

The parts in brackets are guiding the actors. They are not spoken.

Remember
To put in where your scene takes place.

To write the characters' names next to the words they say.

To put in the stage directions in brackets.

Now you try.
1   Write down a conversation that you might have, in the form of a play script.

2   Write a play about a Gang meeting, using the Spark Island Gang as characters. You could act out the play with your friends.

Journalistic writing

You might need to write a report or newspaper article as one of your tasks. It is important to think about the kind of language that you will need to use. Newspapers and reports give us information and need to be clear. In newspapers, exciting headlines are often used to grab the readers' attention.

Look at these headlines.

ELDER IN UNICYCLE DISASTER
GANG SAVE THE DAY
GOOSEBERRY SHORTAGE THREATENS XYBOK

Alliteration is often used in headlines. This means using words with the same beginning consonant, for example:

WIZARD IN WIZZATRON WHIRL
SUPER STRAT SAVES SPIRONAUT

Now you try.

1   Make some headlines of your own. Grab the reader's attention.

2   Read the extract on the right from the *Sparkopolis Times*.

3   Invent your own newspaper. Give it a name and design the front page.

4   Choose a good headline and set out your articles in columns like a real paper.

Remember
Keep your language impersonal. Don't write 'I did' or 'I went' as you would in a story, but write 'There was a ...' or 'An event took place ...'.

SPARK SUCCESS
(Headline in large print to grab attention.)

Spark Island Open Day raises a total of £5000 for the Island's Hospital.
(Slightly smaller print for the first sentence, to draw the reader in.)

The Open Day at Spark Park last Saturday was a great success, say the organisers.
(Write about the event, keeping the language impersonal.)

Crowds of people came from all over Spark Island to see the stalls and exhibitions organised by the Elders.

The biggest money-spinner was the Xybok rides, taking over £1000, which will be used to buy equipment for Spark Island Hospital.
(Pick out certain events to feature.)

An Elder said: 'It was beyond our greatest expectations!'
(Pretend you have interviewed someone who was there.)

Another Open Day is planned for next year.

Report writing

Reports use similar language to newspapers but they try to be objective. That means that they try to be fair and honest in their writing.

Compare these two reports about a book. Which one is more fair and objective?

THE BEST BOOK EVER!!!

I have just finished reading Darles Chickens' new book, 1000 things to do with string. I was unable to put it down. From cover to cover, the book is filled with the most amazing ideas. Darles must be one of the best non-fiction writers ever to have lived. His plan to make a string model of the Eiffel Tower was stunning. I can't wait to try it.

DARLES CHICKENS' LATEST RELEASE

Darles Chickens' latest book is a comprehensive guide to what can be done with a ball of string. He lists 1000 different activities and models to make; some simple like pom-pom dolls and some, such as a suggested model of the Eiffel Tower, seem almost impossible. If you like to make art and craft objects then this would be a good book for you. The book is clearly written, well set out and the instructions are accompanied by illustrations and photographs.

The second report has more information about the book and, although the writer is expressing a personal opinion, it is being done in a more balanced way.

Now you try.

1   Write a report about a book you have read and enjoyed. Try to write about it objectively, saying anything you didn't enjoy about the book as well as what you did enjoy.

Here are some guidelines to help you write a report.

My report is on: _____

Description of the book: (e.g. factual, story, author, etc.) _____

_____

_____

Things I enjoyed: _____

_____

Things I did not enjoy (if any): _____

_____

I would recommend/would not recommend this book for people who:

_____

2   Read reports about books, films or football matches in newspapers and make a note of any good words.

Worlds Apart

Contents

Pages 21-28 can be pulled out to make the texts easier to refer to when you are answering the test questions.

Spacebaby

This extract comes from 'Spacebaby' by Henrietta Banford. The book is about an alien baby who lands on Earth to try and save the world after he has damaged the North Pole whilst playing an interactive computer game on his planet. He has been taken in by a young woman called Tipperary, who realises Spacebaby is an alien; her Aunt Doris, who does not, and Hector the dog. Spacebaby has been given the Earth name, Moses.

In the morning, Aunt Doris asked Tipperary to collect the eggs. 'Friday's Egg Day, dear,' she said, 'and my Egg Ladies will be along any minute.'
'Before we get busy, Aunt Doris, I've got something to tell you,' Tipperary said. 'It's about Moses.'
'If you've got things you want to tell your auntie, you tell 'em, my dear,' Aunt Doris said. 'But you'll have to wait until the Egg Ladies have been.'

Tipperary stomped off to look for eggs. Aunt Doris's hens lay them anywhere. Behind bales of straw. In clumps of nettles. Under the hedge. I was looking forward to seeing the Egg Ladies, but when the first one came into the yard I found out she was just an ordinary person who had come to buy eggs!

The Egg Ladies were mad about me. Some of them spoke a most peculiar language. 'Give your auntie a kiss, my little opsy-popsy poppet! Who's got little squidgum-didgum chubby dubby cheeks then? Who's a little oochy-coochy cuddles?'

One person in the yard was different though. He had glinty grey eyes and a horrible smile - all teeth. Just looking at him gave me the shivers. He hadn't come to buy eggs. He wasn't friendly. And he certainly wasn't glad to see Tipperary. 'That's Silas Stoatwarden,' Aunt Doris whispered when she saw him coming through the gate. 'He lives up at the big house. Studies flying saucers. I wonder what he wants?' We soon found out.

'Who gave you permission to park that eyesore in the spinney?' he snarled at Tipperary, pointing at SOFTIE with a long, thin finger.
'Who gave you permission to ask?' Tipperary snapped back, rubbing at a damp patch I'd left on her shoulder.
'Well you can't stop here,' Stoatwarden said. 'There's a law against it.'
'That's my bus you're talking about,' Tipperary told him, 'and it's parked in my Aunt's spinney.'
'I don't care whose bus it is. Or whose spinney. This is a respectable neighbourhood and I for one won't have it overrun with riffraff in buses! Not them, not their babies and not their mangy dogs!'

Hector began to rumble. Silas Stoatwarden picked up a stick. 'My niece is as good as anyone, Silas Stoatwarden,' Aunt Doris said, hopping between them. 'Better, most likely. So is that baby. And so is the dog. Put that stick down before Hector hurts you, and get off my land.'

'Animals like that one ought to be destroyed,' said Silas Stoatwarden. 'I shouldn't be surprised if something happened to that animal one dark night. Riffraff. The world is full of riffraff.'

He glanced at Tipperary scornfully as he was leaving.

I began to feel a little desperate. I had a nasty feeling that Stoatwarden knew I was an alien. But Aunt Doris still didn't. And I badly needed to start work on the Internet. Time was passing fast - it was Friday lunchtime already - and I was getting nowhere.

'Come on,' I whispered to Tipperary. 'Let's get started on the bus.'

'I've got to explain to Aunt Doris about you and gravity first,' she said. 'I want to break it to her gently. She's not as young as she was. I'll do it as soon as she has counted the egg money.'

As it turned out, Aunt Doris overheard me talking to Bess, her prize Buff Orpington hen, before Tipperary got a chance to tell her anything. I was talking chicken, naturally, but Aunt Doris understood at once that we were in communication.

Bess was telling me where I could find some particularly juicy caterpillars. I was trying to make her understand that I don't eat caterpillars. Hens aren't good at seeing other people's points of view. She kept insisting on how succulent they were - with a hint of pepper to them - because they'd been feeding on cress by the pond.

I kept saying, 'Yes, they're lovely, but I don't eat them.'

Tipperary had left me in a basket, hanging from the apple tree, out of harm's way, while she took the egg money indoors. Bess was perched close by. Suddenly, I looked up and there was Aunt Doris, watching me and Bess with her beady brown eye - not unlike a hen's eye but more friendly.

'Tipperary!' she screeched 'Tipperary! Come out here quick! Your boy Moses is squawking like a chicken! I do believe he's talking to my Bess!'

Tipperary ran up and lifted me out of my basket. She sat down under the apple tree and balanced me on her knees.

'You sit down too, Aunt Doris,' she said.
'Don't speak to me as if I'm queer in the head, girl,' Aunt Doris said, 'because I'm not.'
'I know you're not, Aunt Doris. Moses can talk. He talks to me. He talks to Hector. It's no surprise to me if he can talk to Bess. He could probably talk to an egg.'
'Well, I've tried, Tipperary,' I interrupted. 'But they don't have anything to say unless they're just about to hatch and then it's only "Help!" or "Get me out of here!"'

Aunt Doris sat perfectly still. She didn't look at me or Tipperary. She watched Bess fly down to scratch in the earth under the apple tree. Tipperary took Doris's brown hand and held it.
'I should have told you before,' she said. She told Aunt Doris all about how Hector found me on Mount Wrath. Then I told her all about gravity and the North Pole and how I only had till Saturday night to fix it.

Aunt Doris listened. Then she picked me up and had a good look at me. 'I don't care where you came from, son,' she said. 'You're welcome here.' She kissed me and gave me back to Tipperary. 'I never did trust computers,' she added. Then she went indoors and made a pot of tea.

Tipperary sat me on her lap and held the bottle for me while I drank. I leaned back against her and began to calculate the precise power of the electromagnetic wave I was going to need. It was going to take a big one. I had no idea if my plan would work.

Heavenly Bodies

Earth facts

- Earth is the third planet from the Sun and the fifth largest planet of the solar system. It is the only planet definitely known to support life.
- The distance from the Earth to the Sun is around 149 million kilometres.

- The Earth revolves about the Sun once every $365\frac{1}{4}$ days which is a year. The path of this revolution, the Earth's orbit, is oval in shape. This means the Earth is closer to the Sun in January than it is in July.

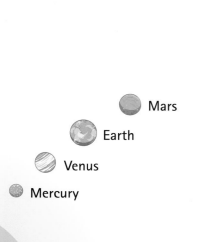

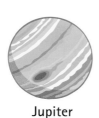

Jupiter

Saturn

Uranus

Neptune Pluto

Mars

Earth

Venus

Mercury

Sun

What is a star?

A star is a hot glowing ball of gas. It gives off light and other forms of electromagnetic radiation whose source is nuclear energy. Stars differ widely in mass or weight, size, temperature and brightness. The Sun is our nearest star and all the planets in our solar system orbit around it.

Why is the Sun so important?

Without the heat and light of the Sun, there would not be life on Earth. Solar energy is used by green plants for photosynthesis.

Is the Sun the brightest star?

The brightest stars are about a million times more powerful than the Sun, while the least bright are only one hundredth as powerful. The biggest stars are hundreds of times greater in size than the Sun. Among the smallest stars, white dwarfs are no larger than a planet. Neutron stars are only a mile or so across. The Sun is a medium-sized star.

Race for Space

Throughout the 50s and 60s, the Americans and Russians wanted to be the first country to get people into space and explore the planets. Here are some facts about their rivalry.

WHEN DID THE SPACE RACE BEGIN?

- The first artificial satellite, Sputnik I, was launched by the Soviet Union on October 4th, 1957.
- Explorer I, the first American satellite, was launched on January 31, 1958.

WHO WAS THE FIRST MAN IN SPACE?

Yuri Gagarin was the first man to travel into space in 1961. He was a Russian cosmonaut.

WHEN DID THE FIRST AMERICAN GO INTO SPACE?

The American Mercury program had its first success in February, 1962, when astronaut John Glenn circled the Earth three times.

WHEN WAS THE FIRST SPACE WALK?

During the second Voskhod flight in March 1965, a Russian cosmonaut left the capsule to make the first spacewalk.

HOW MANY TIMES HAVE WE BEEN TO THE MOON?

Altogether, there were 17 Apollo missions and 6 lunar landings. Apollo 8 was the first space ship to orbit both the Earth and the Moon. On July 20, 1969, astronauts Neil A Armstrong and Edwin (Buzz) Aldrin, Jr, stepped on the Moon as Michael Collins orbited the Moon in the command ship, Apollo 11.

CAN ANYBODY LIVE IN SPACE?

Yes, space stations have been built and are also now being developed which allow a team of people to live and work in space and carry out scientific experiments. They are taken up to the space station in a shuttle and return to Earth in the same way. They can stay there for months at a time.

The Space Station Mir was a Russian space station but astronauts and scientists from many countries, including: the United States, Russia, Japan, Canada, Brazil, and the European Space Agency worked alongside each other. Mir has now fallen back to Earth but the assembly of the International Space Station began in December, 1998, and will be completed in 2004.

WHEN WAS THE FIRST SPACE SHUTTLE LAUNCHED?

The first space shuttle was launched in 1981 and was the first reusable rocket. It gets a 'piggyback' into space from two huge booster rockets and then glides back to Earth at the end of its missions.

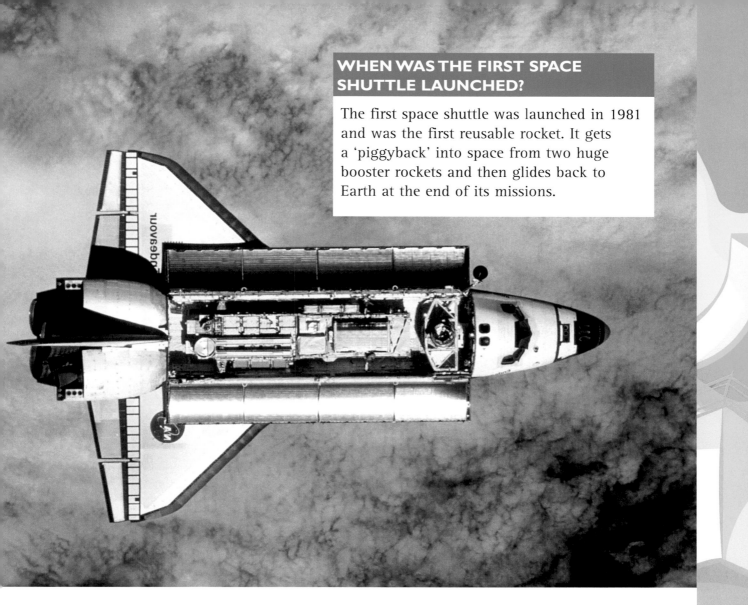

HOW WILL WE FIND OUT MORE ABOUT THE OTHER PLANETS?

The unmanned spacecraft Voyagers 1 and 2, which were launched in 1977, explored Jupiter, Saturn, Uranus and Neptune. They passed as close as 4,800 kilometres to each planet's surface and discovered new rings, magnetic fields, and took photographs of these planets and their moons. The joint United States-European Space Agency probe Cassini, launched in 1997, will explore Saturn, its rings, and some of its moons when it reaches there in 2004.

Blast off!

by Anne Loadman

See me standing proudly on the launch pad,
A silver giant, nose pointing skywards.
Tall as a skyscraper,
Sleek as a thoroughbred,
Straining to shoot beyond the clouds
where I belong.

Small as pins
Crammed into my tip
Are a team of busy people
Preparing for launch.
Anxious but excited
They make their final checks,
Then at last I'll be free.

See my nostrils flaring, steaming,
Dragon's breath on the concrete below
Crowds have gathered, watching, waiting.
Not long now.

Enormous power is surging through me.
Hurry I can't hold on much longer!
5-4-3-2-1- BLAST OFF!
I rise, elegant as a swan,
in a perfect curve.
Released from my chains,
I am FREE!

Letter writing

Letters can be used to:
- share news or information
- express an opinion
- try to persuade someone.

Letters can be formal or informal and you must know how to write each kind.

Formal letters are written to officials, such as councillors, businesses and newspapers. They often start 'Dear Sir/Madam' and end 'Yours faithfully'.

Informal letters are written to friends and family. They often start 'Dear (name of the person)' and end 'Yours sincerely'.

Here is a letter that Zeb wrote to one of the Elders, asking him to extend library opening hours.

What is the purpose of Zeb's letter?

(Write your address and the date.) The Gang House,
Spark Island,
11.11.10

Library Department,
The Sparkanon,
Spark Island.   *(Write the address of the recipient.)*

Dear Elder Xanon, *(Write the name of the person you want to read the letter.)*

(start to write here) I am writing to ask if you could extend the opening hours of the new library in Blackspark Road. *(Explain why you are writing – the purpose of your letter.)*

I would like to see the library open in the evening and at weekends, so that people who work until teatime would be able to use the library. If the library was open on Sundays, then families could visit the library together. I'm sure that you realise the importance of libraries to the people of Sparkopolis and want to encourage new readers. *(Write what you hope will happen as a result of your letter.)* I hope you will consider my proposals and send me a reply.

Yours faithfully, *(Formal ending for a formal letter.)*

Zeb *(Remember to put the name of the sender.)*

Now try this.

1   Plan and write a letter to Strat asking him if you can join the Spark Island Gang. Use persuasive language.

2   Plan and write a letter to your local newspaper, concerning something you feel strongly about, e.g. lack of play facilities, traffic, litter. You might get it published.

3   Plan and write a letter to your favourite sports person or pop star, asking for information about matches, tour dates, new singles etc. You might get a reply!

Diaries

Diaries are more informal and are usually only read by the person who wrote them. Diaries are often written in note form, instead of complete sentences and express the thoughts and feelings of the writer as well as recording events that happened on a particular day.

Nina hasn't told the Gang, but she keeps a diary. She fills it in every night just before she goes to sleep. Here is what she wrote yesterday.

30th Oct.
Today was great! We picked wild raspberries and fed the Xybox. Great! My fingers are still bright red and I've scrubbed them hard! Milo seems a little bit sad today. I think it's because he's not as tall as the rest of us and he couldn't reach the branches when we were climbing trees. I'll talk to him tomorrow.

Now you try.
1   Pretend you are Milo and write your own diary for 30th October. Write down the day's events from his point of view.

30th October

2   Why not keep a diary yourself. It could be about what happens to you each day, or it could be really specific, like writing down what you watch on the television or eat in a week.

Questions about 'Heavenly Bodies' and 'Race for Space'

1   Why has the author organized the text into small boxes/sections?

1

1 mark

2   Why has the author put a question in bold text or in a box at the start of each fact?

2

2 marks

3   Complete the information in this table.

Name	Event	Date
Yuri Gagarin	First man in space	
	Circled the Earth three times	February 1962
International Space Station		1998

3

3 marks

4   In the text it says that the space shuttle gets a 'piggyback' into space from two booster rockets. Why does the author use the word 'piggyback' to describe this?

4

1 mark

5   What is the difference between the information given in 'Race for Space' and that given in 'Heavenly Bodies'?

5

2 marks

6   From 'Heavenly Bodies', find and copy **three** facts about the Sun.

1

2

3

6

3 marks

7 Draw lines to connect the person/object to the correct fact.

Sputnik 1   is the third nearest planet to the Sun

Mir Space Station   flew on Apollo 11

Earth   was the second man to walk on the Moon

Michael Collins   was built by the Russians

Buzz Aldrin   was the first satellite

7

3 marks

8 From 'Heavenly Bodies', find and copy **three** facts about the Earth.

1 _____

2 _____

3 _____

8

3 marks

9 In 'Race for Space' find a word similar in meaning to:

(a) without people _____

(b) made by man _____

(c) to travel around a planet or star _____

(d) can be used again _____

9

4 marks

10 In your opinion, after reading 'Race for Space', what do you think was the greatest achievement and why?

_____

_____

_____

_____

10

3 marks

Questions about 'Blast Off'

1   What is the rocket desperate to do?

1

1 mark

2   Which word best describes the feelings of the rocket?

anxious   worried   excited   upset

2

1 mark

3   This poem has four

lines   scenes   verses   chapters

3

1 mark

4   Who are 'small as pins' in the poem?

4

1 mark

5   Why are the words FREE and BLAST OFF written in capital letters?

5

1 mark

6   Find words or phrases in the text which tell you about the size of the rocket.

6

2 marks

7   This poem uses similes to describe the rocket. Find and copy **three** of them.

7

3 marks

8   Look at the second verse of the poem. How is it different from the rest of the poem?

8

2 marks

PRACTICE WRITING TEST

You will have up to 45 minutes to plan and finish the longer task, and 20 minutes for the shorter task. You should have a break between tasks.

Longer task

*Option 1: The planet Hylax

> It is the year 3050 and you have won a competition to be the first child in space. You will be part of a mission travelling to Hylax, a new planet discovered at the edge of the Milky Way. Write about your journey to the new planet and imagine stepping out onto a planet where no-one else has been.

In your writing:
- describe how you felt when you won and how you feel waiting for take-off
- describe what it is like to travel through space
- describe the planet as you land
- write about any life on Hylax.

You will need to plan:
- who will be in your story
- where the different parts will take place
- what you see, hear and feel.

Plan your story below.

Characters	Settings
Plot	Beginning and ending

You should start to write when you feel ready.
Remember you have only 45 minutes to complete this task.

Note: * From 2003 there will be no choice of activity in the longer or shorter tasks of the National Test for English. However in this book a choice has been given so that a wider range of writing types may be covered. Select either Option 1 or Option 2 for the longer as well as the shorter writing tasks.

Option 2: Lights in the Sky!

> You are outside your house in the evening, when you see a strange light in the sky. It hovers and then seems to land in the playing field nearby. Write an adventure story about the events of that evening.

You will need to think about:
- who will be in your story
- where your story will take place
- what will happen and the order of events
- how to begin and end your story.

Plan your story below.

Characters	Settings
Plot	Beginning and ending

You should start to write when you feel ready.
Remember you only have 45 minutes to complete this task.

Shorter task

Option 1

The Hylaxians are keen to *persuade* space tourists to visit their planet. They have asked you to design a leaflet/brochure telling Earth people about the sights and activities available on their planet.

They particularly want you to mention:
- Hylax is only four light years away
- the temperature is always 70 degrees
- the people are friendly and peace-loving
- the capital city of Irwax has a castle and cathedral (entry to both is free) and lots of gift shops
- the purple sands of Iwash Bay and the sea which is green
- the space zoo in Hylax Town with creatures from all over the galaxy.

Set out this information in the form of a leaflet or poster. You may add details of your own and think of a slogan that will make people want to visit Hylax.

Remember you only have 20 minutes to complete this task.

You may plan your work below.

Plan of my design:

Option 2

Some inhabitants of Hylax have come to Earth for a visit. They are very confused by life here as it is different from their planet. Write some instructions to:
- help a Hylaxian play an Earth game
- show a Hylaxian how to get dressed in Earth clothes
- tell a Hylaxian how to work a television set.

Make your instructions clear and simple. Remember to use commands. Think about the order in which your instructions should come. You may draw a diagram to accompany your instructions, if you have time.

Remember you have 20 minutes to complete this task.

You may plan your work below.

Plan of my instructions, including words I might use:

PRACTICE SPELLING TEST

Follow the passage below as someone reads it to you. When it is read for the second time, try to spell the words which fit in the blank spaces.

THE SOLAR SYSTEM

The solar system in .... we live is made up of the Sun, its planets, natural satellites, asteroids, meteoroids and comets. Each of these .... are held to each other by the force we .... gravity. The Sun is by far the most .... part of the solar system. It is our nearest star. Without the Sun there would be no .... and no .... on Earth.

The other main members of the solar system are the nine major planets. The planets are Mercury, Venus, Earth, Mars, Jupiter, Saturn, Uranus, Neptune and Pluto.

The planets are .... in almost .... orbits based on the force of gravity. The Sun's gravitational pull is the most .... gravitational force in the solar system.

The planets orbit the Sun in the same anticlockwise direction. A planet's year is the time .... for it to complete one full orbit .... the Sun. This varies in length from planet to planet. One Earth year lasts 365 $\frac{1}{4}$ days.

The planets are .... according to their physical properties. The inner planets (Mercury, Venus, Earth and Mars) are called the terrestrial (meaning earthlike) planets. They are dense and small in .... They have solid, rocky crusts and .... insides are made of molten, metallic rocks. Most of the nine major planets have one or more moons. In 1969, Neil Armstrong was the first man to .... on the moon which orbits our Earth.

The planets Jupiter, Saturn, Uranus and Neptune are sometimes .... as the 'gas ....'. Jupiter, is famous for its 'red spot': the site of a huge storm on the planet. Saturn, of course, is famous for its rings. It has been said that if you had a bath large ...., Saturn could float in it because of its low density. Pluto is on the .... of our Solar System and is hard to see clearly, even with modern ....

Note to parents
You will find the complete text for this Spelling text on p3. Read it through once to your child, then on the second read, pause after each underlined word in your text so he or she can fill in the words on this page.

Assessing your child's writing

The way in which children's writing is assessed in the National Tests is changing. From 2003, the marking criteria are specific to the task set and not level specific. This section includes a way of assessing writing, so that an approximate level can be given.

For the longer task, there is a maximum of 28 marks, awarded for sentence structure and punctuation, text structure and organization, and composition and effect. The shorter task carries a possible 12 marks, with sentence structure, punctuation and text organization assessed together and composition and effect being the other component.

To assess your child's work, look at their writing for the following qualities and components, and award marks up to the maximum shown. If your child does not meet the criteria for maximum marks in each section, parental judgement should be exercised to award a reasonable number of marks, based on how far from the ideal their writing is.

Longer task
Sentence structure and punctuation
(maximum 8 marks)
- [ ] Sentences of varying lengths, written with clarity, purpose and effect.
- [ ] Accuracy of syntax and punctuation in sentences, clauses and phrases.

Text structure and organization
(maximum 8 marks)
- [ ] Whole texts are presented effectively, with information, events and ideas sequenced and structured logically.
- [ ] Writing is divided into paragraphs which follow on from each other and are appropriate divisions of the text.

Composition and effect
(maximum 12 marks)
- [ ] Imaginative, interesting and thoughtful texts with good use of language, including adjectives, adverbs etc.
- [ ] Texts are appropriate to purpose and to the reader for which they are intended.

Shorter task
Sentence structure, punctuation and text organization
(maximum 4 marks)
- [ ] Sentences of varying lengths, written with clarity, purpose and effect.
- [ ] Accuracy of syntax and punctuation in sentences, clauses and phrases.
- [ ] Writing is divided into paragraphs which follow on from each other and are appropriate divisions of the text.

Composition and effect
(maximum 8 marks)
- [ ] Imaginative, interesting and thoughtful texts with good use of language, including adjectives, adverbs etc.
- [ ] Texts are appropriate to purpose and to the reader for which they are intended

A more detailed marking system, explaining the changes more fully, can be obtained from the QCA website: www.qca.org.uk/ca/tests/2003sample

Awarding a level

Once you have added up all the comprehension marks for the Practice Test (maximum 50 marks) and have made an assessment of your child's writing for the longer and shorter task, there are two more areas to assess before an approximate level can be awarded.

Spelling
The spelling test is marked out of 20, but, from 2003, a maximum of seven marks will be awarded. The marks will be aggregated to a scale of one to seven marks, along these lines:

19-20 correct spellings – 7 marks   16-18 correct spellings – 6 marks
13-15 correct spellings – 5 marks   10-12 correct spellings – 4 marks
7-9 correct spellings – 3 marks   6-8 correct spellings – 2 marks
5 and below – 1 mark

Handwriting
Handwriting is no longer assessed separately. To assess your child's handwriting, choose a few sentences from one of the writing tasks, where his or her best writing appears.

Handwriting now carries a maximum of three marks:
1 mark: Handwriting is legible and shows some regularity of size and spacing. Overall, however, the writing is uneven and disjointed.
2 marks: Handwriting is regular with some flow and movement. There is some variation in size, but letters and words are usually appropriate in size and position.
3 marks: Handwriting is consistent and fluent with letters and words appropriately placed. There is evidence of a personal style, usually joined, which engages the reader. Handwriting is clear and letters well-formed.

Once all these assessments have been made and **a score out of 100** arrived at, an approximate level may be awarded. It is difficult to be precise about the exact marks which constitute a particular level as each year the thresholds for a level change by two or three marks either way, according to national achievement.
Therefore these marks and levels are to be used only as a guide.

78-80+ marks – expected Level 5
48-52 marks up to 78-80 marks – expected Level 4
28 marks up to 48-52 marks – expected Level 3
Below 28 marks – expected level 2 or below

Children who achieve below 25 marks may not sit their English National Test paper, but will be assessed by the teacher, who awards a Level 2 on their behalf.

Once you have assessed your child's strengths and weaknesses, you will know the areas for development, and be able to give your child more practice in the necessary areas.

Answers

Reading practice

Page 5   Multiple-choice question
Chloe decided she would pretend that she was sick. Mr. Rogers kept you in if you forgot your homework twice.

Page 5   Finding words
1 absent-minded
2 worried
3 Chloe had forgotten her homework – again! (Accept any answer that refers to one of her excuses which suggests she had forgotten her homework before.)

Page 6
1 The Ancient Greeks thought the snake represented healing.
2 reptiles
3 the viper or adder
4 'shed' means lost, got rid of, removed (Accept any similar answer.)

Page 7   Sequencing or matching
2 4 The Malvos went to the Crombies' houses.
   7 The Malvos had to do jobs for a week.
   6 The Gang went to look for the Malvos.
   2 The Malvos burst balloons.
   5 Everyone came out to see what was going on.
   3 The Malvos hid the Spironauts' jetpacks.
   1 It was quiet in Sparkopolis.
3 The Malvos – bursting balloons
   The Malvos – hiding jetpacks
   The Crombies – reading quietly
   The Gang – found the Malvos
   The Elders – heard about the disturbance

Page 8   Thanks to Science
5 Michael Faraday   Built the first dynamo   1831
   Galileo Galilei   Planets orbited the Sun   1610
   Isaac Newton   Light is made of different colours   1664-1666
   Louis Pasteur   Principles of vaccination   1881
6 Planets orbited the sun
7 (a) Faraday: 40; Galilei: 46; Newton: 22-24; Pasteur: 59   (b) Isaac Newton lived the longest
8 (open answer)

Page 9   Short questions – HiYa! Magazine
2 It is the headline; to grab the reader's attention; for emphasis; it is the most important word on the page (Accept any similar answer.)
3 (a) The information is organized in bullet points, with each section introduced by a sub-heading.
   (b) It is clear; it is easy to read; it tells you what you can read about; it makes you want to know more about the articles. (Accept any similar answer.)
4 For emphasis; to show they are the only magazine that has these stories; to make you think there are lots of articles; they are important words.

Spelling practice

Page 33   Double consonants: Short vowels
1 (a) a small child – toddler   (b) chewy sweet – toffee
   (c) a dog's home – kennel

Page 33   Long vowels

c	l	u	e	a	d	e	m	b	w	y	o
s	t	e	x	d	i	v	i	d	e	e	m
t	s	l	p	v	s	a	d	b	r	y	i
h	g	d	l	i	g	j	k	i	b	n	s
e	e	b	o	c	r	e	f	u	s	e	t
s	w	r	d	e	a	i	y	v	s	g	a
e	q	e	e	x	c	u	s	e	m	o	k
a	l	o	n	e	e	t	y	d	i	l	e
r	f	b	w	p	a	d	e	j	n	o	p
d	c	d	q	s	t	r	a	n	g	e	r

Page 34   Silent letters
1 (a) Listen   (b) write   (c) guitar, Christmas

Page 34   Soft letters
glitter (h)   gymnast (s)   palace (s)   fancy (s)
generous (s)   clever (h)   giant (s)   growth (h)
receive (s)   circle (s) for the first c, (h) for the second,
creature (h)   message (s)

Page 35   Prefixes and suffixes
1 (a) respectable   (b) active/action   (c) usherette
   (d) disgraceful
2 (a) sensible   (b) probable   (c) attainable
   (d) reasonable   (e) possible   (f) reliable
   (g) impossible   (h) responsible

Page 36   Plurals -ies
1 cherries, ladies, lorries
2 thieves, halves, hooves
3 glasses, watches, crashes, potatoes

Practice test

Page 37   Spacebaby
1 The eggs were bought by Egg Ladies.
2 SOFTIE was a bus.
3 Hector had found Moses on Mount Wrath.
4 Behind bales of straw; in clumps of nettles; under the hedge. (Accept on the farm.)
5 5 Aunt Doris realises Moses can speak.
   2 Silas Stoatwarden arives.
   4 Moses talks to Bess the hen.
   1 The Egg Ladies arrive.
   3 Tipperary puts Moses on a tree branch.
6 'out of harm's way' means to put in a safe place; put away from danger; so he wouldn't get hurt. (Accept any similar answer.)

7   **Award 1 mark** for a short, factual answer, e.g. He spoke crossly to Tipperary and the Egg Ladies loved her.

Award 2 marks for an answer which shows more than one example of Silas' character; e.g. He had glinty eyes and his smile was unfriendly. He complained about everything.

Award 3 marks for a full answer with comparisons and detail, e.g. the Egg Ladies were friendly and he was not; the Egg Ladies spoke nicely and he was cross and shouted. He was snobby because he talked about 'riff-raff' as if he was better than anyone.

8   **Award 1 mark** for a simple answer, e.g. she was shocked or surprised.

Award 2 marks for an answer which satisfies both parts of the question, e.g. Aunt Doris was shocked at first, but then she calmed down and kissed him.

Award 3 marks for a full and detailed answer, perhaps with words taken from the text, e.g. Aunt Doris was surprised to see Moses talking to the chicken, but she didn't think she was going mad. She said, 'Don't speak to me as if I'm queer in the head, girl'. When she calmed down and Moses had explained the situation to her, she was loving to Moses and said he was welcome to stay there.

Page 39   Heavenly Bodies and Race for Space

1   Each box or section contains a different fact or facts about a different part of space. It is clear and easy to read; it is easy to find the information you want. (Accept any similar answer.)

2   The words in bold/in boxes are used so that they are emphasized, like subheadings, and you can easily find the information you want. They make you want to find out the answers and make you read on. They separate the questions from the answers and make the text easy to follow. (Accept any similar answer.)

3
Yuri Gagarin	First man in space	1961
John Glenn	Circled the Earth three times	February 1962
International Space Station	Assembly began	1998

4   The author uses the word 'piggyback' because the space shuttle is attached to the back of two large booster rockets to launch it into space and the shuttle looks like it is getting a piggyback. (Accept any similar answer.)

5   In Race for Space, the facts are about the American and Russian astronauts and cosmonauts who risked their lives to explore space; whereas Heavenly Bodies is about the stars and the planets. (Accept any similar answer.)

6   Possible answers: the Sun is a medium-sized star; the distance from the Sun to Earth is about 149 million kilometres; the Sun is our nearest star; the Sun is a glowing ball of hot gas; all planets in our solar system orbit round the Sun; without the heat and light from the Sun, there would be no life on Earth.

7   Sputnik 1 – was the first satellite.
Mir Space Station – was built by the Russians.
Earth – is the third nearest planet to the Sun.
Michael Collins – flew on Apollo 11.
Buzz Aldrin – was the second man to walk on the Moon

8   Earth is the third planet away from the Sun; the Earth revolves around the Sun once every $365\frac{1}{4}$ days; Earth needs the heat and light from the Sun; Earth is the only planet known to have life; the Earth is closer to the Sun in January than July; the Earth's orbit is oval in shape. (Accept any similar answer.)

9   (a) without people – unmanned
(b) made by man – artificial
(c) to travel round a planet or a star – orbit
(d) can be used again – reusable

10 **Award 1 mark** for a simple, factual answer that expresses the child's opinion.

Award 2 marks for an answer supported by a reason.

Award 3 marks for an answer that expresses the child's opinion, backed up by a well thought-out reason and possibly comparison to some of the other achievements.

Page 41   Blast Off!

1   The rocket is desperate to take off/break free/escape its chains.

2   excited

3   verses

4   the astronauts

5   For emphasis/as if the rocket is shouting etc.

6   Accept: silver giant; tall as a skyscraper.

7   Similes: tall as a skyscraper; sleek as a thoroughbred; small as pins; or elegant as a swan.

8   The second verse of the poem deals with the astronauts and how they are feeling, whereas the other verses deal with the feelings of the rocket.